It was sports day.

1

Wilma was in the long jump.

She came first.

Wilf and Chip were in a race. They came second.

"Hooray!" shouted Kipper.

Dad was in the egg and spoon
race. He came third.

"Well done, Dad," shouted Wilf.

Mum was in a race.

"Oh no!" said Wilma.

Mum came last.

"Poor old Mum," said Wilf.

Mum was disappointed.

"What a shame!" said Dad.

Dad put a blindfold on Mum.

Wilf and Wilma had a surprise.

"Good old Mum," said everyone.